100 days of BIBLE VERSE JOURNALING

A SCRIPTURE MEMORY & KEEPSAKE NOTEBOOK

WRITTEN & DESIGNED BY SHALANA FRISBY

WWW.123JOURNALIT.COM

Don't forget to grab your bonus freebies today!

www.123JournalIt.com / FREEBIES

SCRIPTURE FLASHCARDS - BIBLE READING PROMPTS - JOURNALING PAGES

More information at: www.123journalit.com

First Printing: June 2018
1 2 3 Journal It Publishing

ISBN-13: 978-1-947209-78-7

8.5-inch Square Format Size with the Black & Green Cover Design
From the *Women's Devotional Workbooks* Series

This journal

BELONGS TO

_____

How to use
THIS JOURNAL

Write one scripture daily, reflect on its meaning, and then practice to learn it using the checklist. To help memorize scripture better, continue doing the practice & learn checklist on each verse for several days in a row.

NEED SOMEWHERE TO START?   TRY THESE VERSES:

Prayer & Pursuing God
1. Romans 8:26
2. Matthew 6:6
3. James 1:6
4. Luke 11:13
5. Psalm 5:3
6. Matthew 7:7
7. Psalm 17:6
8. James 5:16
9. 1 Thessalonians 5:17
10. Colossians 4:2
11. Ephesians 6:18
12. Lamentations 3:25

Discernment & Learning
1. Proverbs 3:5
2. Psalm 119:11
3. 1 Corinthians 2:14
4. Joshua 1:8
5. Psalm 86:11
6. Hebrews 4:12
7. 2 Timothy 3:16
8. 1 Peter 3:15
9. Matthew 4:4
10. Isaiah 55:11
11. Romans 15:4
12. Psalm 32:8

Record of My 100 Bible Verses

BIBLE VERSE: _____ DATE: _____

_____
_____
_____
_____
_____
_____
_____
_____
_____

WHAT DOES iT MEAN & HOW CAN I APPLY iT TO MY LiFE TODAY?

_____
_____
_____
_____
_____
_____

PRACTICE & LEARN:

- ☑ SAY iT OUT LOUD TWiCE
- ☑ DRAW OR DOODLE iT
- ☑ USE iT iN A PRAYER
- ☑ SHARE iT WiTH OTHERS

NOTES:

BIBLE VERSE: _____   DATE: _____

_____
_____
_____
_____
_____
_____
_____
_____

WHAT DOES IT MEAN & HOW CAN I APPLY IT TO MY LIFE TODAY?

_____

_____

_____

_____

_____

_____

_____

PRACTICE & LEARN:

☐ SAY IT OUT LOUD TWICE

☐ DRAW OR DOODLE IT

☐ USE IT IN A PRAYER

☐ SHARE IT WITH OTHERS

NOTES:

BIBLE VERSE: _____ DATE: _____

_____
_____
_____
_____
_____
_____
_____
_____
_____

WHAT DOES IT MEAN & HOW CAN I APPLY IT TO MY LIFE TODAY?

_____
_____
_____
_____
_____
_____
_____
_____

PRACTICE & LEARN:

- ☐ SAY IT OUT LOUD TWICE
- ☐ DRAW OR DOODLE IT
- ☐ USE IT IN A PRAYER
- ☐ SHARE IT WITH OTHERS

NOTES:

BIBLE VERSE: _____ DATE: _____

_____

_____

_____

_____

_____

_____

_____

WHAT DOES IT MEAN & HOW CAN I APPLY IT TO MY LIFE TODAY?

_____

_____

_____

_____

_____

_____

_____

_____

PRACTICE & LEARN:

- ☐ SAY IT OUT LOUD TWICE
- ☐ DRAW OR DOODLE IT
- ☐ USE IT IN A PRAYER
- ☐ SHARE IT WITH OTHERS

NOTES:

BIBLE VERSE: _____ DATE: _____

_____

_____

_____

_____

_____

_____

_____

_____

WHAT DOES IT MEAN & HOW CAN I APPLY IT TO MY LIFE TODAY?

_____

_____

_____

_____

_____

_____

_____

PRACTICE & LEARN:

- ☐ SAY IT OUT LOUD TWICE
- ☐ DRAW OR DOODLE IT
- ☐ USE IT IN A PRAYER
- ☐ SHARE IT WITH OTHERS

NOTES:

BIBLE VERSE: _____ DATE: _____

_____

_____

_____

_____

_____

_____

_____

_____

_____

WHAT DOES IT MEAN & HOW CAN I APPLY IT TO MY LIFE TODAY?

_____

_____

_____

_____

_____

_____

_____

_____

PRACTICE & LEARN:

- ☐ SAY IT OUT LOUD TWICE
- ☐ DRAW OR DOODLE IT
- ☐ USE IT IN A PRAYER
- ☐ SHARE IT WITH OTHERS

NOTES:

BIBLE VERSE: _____ DATE: ....

_____
_____
_____
_____
_____
_____
_____
_____

WHAT DOES IT MEAN & HOW CAN I APPLY IT TO MY LIFE TODAY?

_____

_____

_____

_____

_____

_____

_____

PRACTICE & LEARN:

☐ SAY IT OUT LOUD TWICE

☐ DRAW OR DOODLE IT

☐ USE IT IN A PRAYER

☐ SHARE IT WITH OTHERS

NOTES:

BIBLE VERSE: _____ DATE: _____

_____

_____

_____

_____

_____

_____

_____

_____

WHAT DOES IT MEAN & HOW CAN I APPLY IT TO MY LIFE TODAY?

_____

_____

_____

_____

_____

_____

_____

PRACTICE & LEARN:

☐ SAY IT OUT LOUD TWICE

☐ DRAW OR DOODLE IT

☐ USE IT IN A PRAYER

☐ SHARE IT WITH OTHERS

NOTES:

BIBLE VERSE: _____ DATE: _____

_____
_____
_____
_____
_____
_____
_____
_____

WHAT DOES IT MEAN & HOW CAN I APPLY IT TO MY LIFE TODAY?

_____
_____
_____
_____
_____
_____
_____

PRACTICE & LEARN:

- ☐ SAY IT OUT LOUD TWICE
- ☐ DRAW OR DOODLE IT
- ☐ USE IT IN A PRAYER
- ☐ SHARE IT WITH OTHERS

NOTES:

BIBLE VERSE: _____ DATE: _____

_____

_____

_____

_____

_____

_____

_____

_____

WHAT DOES IT MEAN & HOW CAN I APPLY IT TO MY LIFE TODAY?

_____

_____

_____

_____

_____

_____

_____

PRACTICE & LEARN:

- ☐ SAY IT OUT LOUD TWICE
- ☐ DRAW OR DOODLE IT
- ☐ USE IT IN A PRAYER
- ☐ SHARE IT WITH OTHERS

NOTES:

BIBLE VERSE: _____ DATE: _____

_____

_____

_____

_____

_____

_____

_____

_____

WHAT DOES IT MEAN & HOW CAN I APPLY IT TO MY LIFE TODAY?

_____

_____

_____

_____

_____

_____

_____

PRACTICE & LEARN:

- ☐ SAY IT OUT LOUD TWICE
- ☐ DRAW OR DOODLE IT
- ☐ USE IT IN A PRAYER
- ☐ SHARE IT WITH OTHERS

NOTES:

BIBLE VERSE: _____   ((DATE: _____))

_____
_____
_____
_____
_____
_____
_____
_____

WHAT DOES IT MEAN & HOW CAN I APPLY IT TO MY LIFE TODAY?

_____   PRACTICE & LEARN:
_____
_____   ☐ SAY IT OUT LOUD TWICE
_____
_____   ☐ DRAW OR DOODLE IT
_____
_____   ☐ USE IT IN A PRAYER
_____
                                            ☐ SHARE IT WITH OTHERS

NOTES:

BIBLE VERSE: _____ DATE: _____

_____

_____

_____

_____

_____

_____

_____

WHAT DOES IT MEAN & HOW CAN I APPLY IT TO MY LIFE TODAY?

_____

_____

_____

_____

_____

_____

_____

PRACTICE & LEARN:

- ☐ SAY IT OUT LOUD TWICE
- ☐ DRAW OR DOODLE IT
- ☐ USE IT IN A PRAYER
- ☐ SHARE IT WITH OTHERS

NOTES:

BIBLE VERSE: _____ DATE: _____

_____
_____
_____
_____
_____
_____
_____
_____
_____

WHAT DOES IT MEAN & HOW CAN I APPLY IT TO MY LIFE TODAY?

_____
_____
_____
_____
_____
_____
_____

PRACTICE & LEARN:

- ☐ SAY IT OUT LOUD TWICE
- ☐ DRAW OR DOODLE IT
- ☐ USE IT IN A PRAYER
- ☐ SHARE IT WITH OTHERS

NOTES:

BIBLE VERSE: _____ DATE: _____

_____
_____
_____
_____
_____
_____
_____
_____

WHAT DOES IT MEAN & HOW CAN I APPLY IT TO MY LIFE TODAY?

_____
_____
_____
_____
_____
_____
_____
_____

PRACTICE & LEARN:

☐ SAY IT OUT LOUD TWICE

☐ DRAW OR DOODLE IT

☐ USE IT IN A PRAYER

☐ SHARE IT WITH OTHERS

NOTES:

BIBLE VERSE: _____ DATE: _____

_____
_____
_____
_____
_____
_____
_____
_____

WHAT DOES IT MEAN & HOW CAN I APPLY IT TO MY LIFE TODAY?

_____
_____
_____
_____
_____
_____
_____
_____

PRACTICE & LEARN:

☐ SAY IT OUT LOUD TWICE

☐ DRAW OR DOODLE IT

☐ USE IT IN A PRAYER

☐ SHARE IT WITH OTHERS

NOTES:

BIBLE VERSE: _____ DATE: _____

_____

_____

_____

_____

_____

_____

_____

_____

WHAT DOES IT MEAN & HOW CAN I APPLY IT TO MY LIFE TODAY?

_____

_____

_____

_____

_____

_____

PRACTICE & LEARN:

- ☐ SAY IT OUT LOUD TWICE
- ☐ DRAW OR DOODLE IT
- ☐ USE IT IN A PRAYER
- ☐ SHARE IT WITH OTHERS

NOTES:

BIBLE VERSE: _____ DATE: _____

_____
_____
_____
_____
_____
_____
_____
_____
_____

WHAT DOES IT MEAN & HOW CAN I APPLY IT TO MY LIFE TODAY?

_____
_____
_____
_____
_____
_____
_____
_____

PRACTICE & LEARN:

- ☐ SAY IT OUT LOUD TWICE
- ☐ DRAW OR DOODLE IT
- ☐ USE IT IN A PRAYER
- ☐ SHARE IT WITH OTHERS

NOTES:

BIBLE VERSE: _____ DATE: _____

_____

_____

_____

_____

_____

_____

_____

_____

WHAT DOES IT MEAN & HOW CAN I APPLY IT TO MY LIFE TODAY?

_____

_____

_____

_____

_____

_____

_____

PRACTICE & LEARN:

- ☐ SAY IT OUT LOUD TWICE
- ☐ DRAW OR DOODLE IT
- ☐ USE IT IN A PRAYER
- ☐ SHARE IT WITH OTHERS

NOTES:

BIBLE VERSE: _____ DATE: _____

_____

_____

_____

_____

_____

_____

_____

_____

WHAT DOES IT MEAN & HOW CAN I APPLY IT TO MY LIFE TODAY?

_____

_____

_____

_____

_____

_____

_____

PRACTICE & LEARN:

☐ SAY IT OUT LOUD TWICE

☐ DRAW OR DOODLE IT

☐ USE IT IN A PRAYER

☐ SHARE IT WITH OTHERS

NOTES:

BIBLE VERSE: _____ DATE: _____

_____
_____
_____
_____
_____
_____
_____

WHAT DOES IT MEAN & HOW CAN I APPLY IT TO MY LIFE TODAY?

_____
_____
_____
_____
_____
_____

PRACTICE & LEARN:

☐ SAY IT OUT LOUD TWICE

☐ DRAW OR DOODLE IT

☐ USE IT IN A PRAYER

☐ SHARE IT WITH OTHERS

NOTES:

BIBLE VERSE: _____ DATE: _____

_____

_____

_____

_____

_____

_____

_____

_____

WHAT DOES IT MEAN & HOW CAN I APPLY IT TO MY LIFE TODAY?

_____

_____

_____

_____

_____

_____

PRACTICE & LEARN:

- ☐ SAY IT OUT LOUD TWICE
- ☐ DRAW OR DOODLE IT
- ☐ USE IT IN A PRAYER
- ☐ SHARE IT WITH OTHERS

NOTES:

BIBLE VERSE: _____ DATE: _____

_____
_____
_____
_____
_____
_____
_____
_____
_____

WHAT DOES IT MEAN & HOW CAN I APPLY IT TO MY LIFE TODAY?

_____
_____
_____
_____
_____
_____

PRACTICE & LEARN:

- ☐ SAY IT OUT LOUD TWICE
- ☐ DRAW OR DOODLE IT
- ☐ USE IT IN A PRAYER
- ☐ SHARE IT WITH OTHERS

NOTES:

BIBLE VERSE: _____ DATE: _____

_____

_____

_____

_____

_____

_____

_____

WHAT DOES IT MEAN & HOW CAN I APPLY IT TO MY LIFE TODAY?

_____

_____

_____

_____

_____

_____

_____

_____

PRACTICE & LEARN:

- ☐ SAY IT OUT LOUD TWICE
- ☐ DRAW OR DOODLE IT
- ☐ USE IT IN A PRAYER
- ☐ SHARE IT WITH OTHERS

NOTES:

BIBLE VERSE: _____ DATE: _____

_____
_____
_____
_____
_____
_____
_____
_____

WHAT DOES iT MEAN & HOW CAN i APPLY iT TO MY LiFE TODAY?

_____
_____
_____
_____
_____
_____
_____

PRACTICE & LEARN:

- ☐ SAY iT OUT LOUD TWiCE
- ☐ DRAW OR DOODLE iT
- ☐ USE iT iN A PRAYER
- ☐ SHARE iT WiTH OTHERS

NOTES:

BIBLE VERSE: _____ DATE: _____

_____

_____

_____

_____

_____

_____

_____

_____

WHAT DOES IT MEAN & HOW CAN I APPLY IT TO MY LIFE TODAY?

_____

_____

_____

_____

_____

_____

_____

PRACTICE & LEARN:

- ☐ SAY IT OUT LOUD TWICE
- ☐ DRAW OR DOODLE IT
- ☐ USE IT IN A PRAYER
- ☐ SHARE IT WITH OTHERS

NOTES:

BIBLE VERSE: _____ DATE: _____

_____
_____
_____
_____
_____
_____
_____
_____

WHAT DOES IT MEAN & HOW CAN I APPLY IT TO MY LIFE TODAY?

_____

_____

_____

_____

_____

_____

_____

PRACTICE & LEARN:

- ☐ SAY IT OUT LOUD TWICE
- ☐ DRAW OR DOODLE IT
- ☐ USE IT IN A PRAYER
- ☐ SHARE IT WITH OTHERS

NOTES:

BIBLE VERSE: _____ DATE: _____

_____

_____

_____

_____

_____

_____

_____

_____

WHAT DOES IT MEAN & HOW CAN I APPLY IT TO MY LIFE TODAY?

_____

_____

_____

_____

_____

_____

_____

_____

PRACTICE & LEARN:

☐ SAY IT OUT LOUD TWICE

☐ DRAW OR DOODLE IT

☐ USE IT IN A PRAYER

☐ SHARE IT WITH OTHERS

NOTES:

BIBLE VERSE: _____ DATE: _____

_____
_____
_____
_____
_____
_____
_____
_____

WHAT DOES IT MEAN & HOW CAN I APPLY IT TO MY LIFE TODAY?

_____
_____
_____
_____
_____
_____
_____

PRACTICE & LEARN:

- ☐ SAY IT OUT LOUD TWICE
- ☐ DRAW OR DOODLE IT
- ☐ USE IT IN A PRAYER
- ☐ SHARE IT WITH OTHERS

NOTES:

BIBLE VERSE: _____ DATE: _____

_____

_____

_____

_____

_____

_____

_____

_____

WHAT DOES IT MEAN & HOW CAN I APPLY IT TO MY LIFE TODAY?

_____

_____

_____

_____

_____

_____

_____

PRACTICE & LEARN:

- ☐ SAY IT OUT LOUD TWICE
- ☐ DRAW OR DOODLE IT
- ☐ USE IT IN A PRAYER
- ☐ SHARE IT WITH OTHERS

NOTES:

BIBLE VERSE: _____ DATE: _____

_____
_____
_____
_____
_____
_____
_____
_____
_____

WHAT DOES iT MEAN & HOW CAN I APPLY iT TO MY LiFE TODAY?

_____
_____
_____
_____
_____
_____
_____

PRACTICE & LEARN:

☐ SAY iT OUT LOUD TWiCE

☐ DRAW OR DOODLE iT

☐ USE iT iN A PRAYER

☐ SHARE iT WiTH OTHERS

NOTES:

BIBLE VERSE: _____ DATE: _____

_____

_____

_____

_____

_____

_____

_____

_____

WHAT DOES IT MEAN & HOW CAN I APPLY IT TO MY LIFE TODAY?

_____

_____

_____

_____

_____

_____

PRACTICE & LEARN:

☐ SAY IT OUT LOUD TWICE

☐ DRAW OR DOODLE IT

☐ USE IT IN A PRAYER

☐ SHARE IT WITH OTHERS

NOTES:

BIBLE VERSE: _____   DATE: _____

_____

_____

_____

_____

_____

_____

_____

WHAT DOES IT MEAN & HOW CAN I APPLY IT TO MY LIFE TODAY?

_____

_____

_____

_____

_____

_____

PRACTICE & LEARN:

☐ SAY IT OUT LOUD TWICE

☐ DRAW OR DOODLE IT

☐ USE IT IN A PRAYER

☐ SHARE IT WITH OTHERS

NOTES:

BIBLE VERSE: _____ DATE: _____

_____
_____
_____
_____
_____
_____
_____
_____

WHAT DOES IT MEAN & HOW CAN I APPLY IT TO MY LIFE TODAY?

_____
_____
_____
_____
_____
_____
_____

PRACTICE & LEARN:

- ☐ SAY IT OUT LOUD TWICE
- ☐ DRAW OR DOODLE IT
- ☐ USE IT IN A PRAYER
- ☐ SHARE IT WITH OTHERS

NOTES:

BIBLE VERSE: _____ DATE: _____

_____

_____

_____

_____

_____

_____

_____

_____

WHAT DOES IT MEAN & HOW CAN I APPLY IT TO MY LIFE TODAY?

_____

_____

_____

_____

_____

_____

_____

PRACTICE & LEARN:

- ☐ SAY IT OUT LOUD TWICE
- ☐ DRAW OR DOODLE IT
- ☐ USE IT IN A PRAYER
- ☐ SHARE IT WITH OTHERS

NOTES:

BIBLE VERSE: _____ DATE: _____

_____
_____
_____
_____
_____
_____
_____
_____

WHAT DOES IT MEAN & HOW CAN I APPLY IT TO MY LIFE TODAY?

_____
_____
_____
_____
_____
_____
_____
_____

PRACTICE & LEARN:

☐ SAY IT OUT LOUD TWICE

☐ DRAW OR DOODLE IT

☐ USE IT IN A PRAYER

☐ SHARE IT WITH OTHERS

NOTES:

BIBLE VERSE: _____ (DATE: _____)

_____
_____
_____
_____
_____
_____
_____
_____

WHAT DOES IT MEAN & HOW CAN I APPLY IT TO MY LIFE TODAY?
_____

PRACTICE & LEARN:

- ☒ SAY IT OUT LOUD TWICE
- ☒ DRAW OR DOODLE IT
- ☒ USE IT IN A PRAYER
- ☒ SHARE IT WITH OTHERS

NOTES:

BIBLE VERSE: _____ (DATE: _____)

_____
_____
_____
_____
_____
_____
_____
_____
_____

WHAT DOES IT MEAN & HOW CAN I APPLY IT TO MY LIFE TODAY?

_____   **PRACTICE & LEARN:**
_____
_____   ☐ SAY IT OUT LOUD TWICE
_____
_____   ☐ DRAW OR DOODLE IT
_____
_____   ☐ USE IT IN A PRAYER
_____
                                                ☐ SHARE IT WITH OTHERS

NOTES:

BIBLE VERSE: _____ DATE: _____

_____
_____
_____
_____
_____
_____
_____
_____

WHAT DOES IT MEAN & HOW CAN I APPLY IT TO MY LIFE TODAY?

_____

_____

_____

_____

_____

_____

_____

PRACTICE & LEARN:

- ☐ SAY IT OUT LOUD TWICE
- ☐ DRAW OR DOODLE IT
- ☐ USE IT IN A PRAYER
- ☐ SHARE IT WITH OTHERS

NOTES:

BIBLE VERSE: _____ DATE: _____

_____
_____
_____
_____
_____
_____
_____
_____

WHAT DOES IT MEAN & HOW CAN I APPLY IT TO MY LIFE TODAY?

_____
_____
_____
_____
_____
_____
_____
_____

PRACTICE & LEARN:

- ☐ SAY IT OUT LOUD TWICE
- ☐ DRAW OR DOODLE IT
- ☐ USE IT IN A PRAYER
- ☐ SHARE IT WITH OTHERS

NOTES:

BIBLE VERSE: _____ DATE: _____

_____
_____
_____
_____
_____
_____
_____
_____
_____

WHAT DOES IT MEAN & HOW CAN I APPLY IT TO MY LIFE TODAY?

_____

PRACTICE & LEARN:

- ☑ SAY IT OUT LOUD TWICE
- ☑ DRAW OR DOODLE IT
- ☑ USE IT IN A PRAYER
- ☑ SHARE IT WITH OTHERS

NOTES:

BIBLE VERSE: _____ (DATE: _____)

_____
_____
_____
_____
_____
_____
_____
_____
_____

WHAT DOES IT MEAN & HOW CAN I APPLY IT TO MY LIFE TODAY?

_____
_____
_____
_____
_____
_____

PRACTICE & LEARN:

- ☐ SAY IT OUT LOUD TWICE
- ☐ DRAW OR DOODLE IT
- ☐ USE IT IN A PRAYER
- ☐ SHARE IT WITH OTHERS

NOTES:

BIBLE VERSE: _____ DATE: _____

_____

_____

_____

_____

_____

_____

_____

_____

WHAT DOES IT MEAN & HOW CAN I APPLY IT TO MY LIFE TODAY?

_____

_____

_____

_____

_____

_____

PRACTICE & LEARN:

- ☐ SAY IT OUT LOUD TWICE
- ☐ DRAW OR DOODLE IT
- ☐ USE IT IN A PRAYER
- ☐ SHARE IT WITH OTHERS

NOTES:

BIBLE VERSE: _____ DATE: _____

_____

_____

_____

_____

_____

_____

_____

_____

WHAT DOES IT MEAN & HOW CAN I APPLY IT TO MY LIFE TODAY?

_____

_____

_____

_____

_____

_____

PRACTICE & LEARN:

☐ SAY IT OUT LOUD TWICE

☐ DRAW OR DOODLE IT

☐ USE IT IN A PRAYER

☐ SHARE IT WITH OTHERS

NOTES:

BIBLE VERSE: _____ DATE: _____

_____
_____
_____
_____
_____
_____
_____
_____
_____

WHAT DOES IT MEAN & HOW CAN I APPLY IT TO MY LIFE TODAY?

_____
_____
_____
_____
_____
_____
_____

PRACTICE & LEARN:

- ☐ SAY IT OUT LOUD TWICE
- ☐ DRAW OR DOODLE IT
- ☐ USE IT IN A PRAYER
- ☐ SHARE IT WITH OTHERS

NOTES:

BIBLE VERSE: _____ DATE: _____

_____

_____

_____

_____

_____

_____

_____

_____

_____

WHAT DOES IT MEAN & HOW CAN I APPLY IT TO MY LIFE TODAY?

_____

_____

_____

_____

_____

_____

_____

PRACTICE & LEARN:

- ☐ SAY IT OUT LOUD TWICE
- ☐ DRAW OR DOODLE IT
- ☐ USE IT IN A PRAYER
- ☐ SHARE IT WITH OTHERS

NOTES:

BIBLE VERSE: _____ DATE: _____

_____

_____

_____

_____

_____

_____

_____

_____

WHAT DOES IT MEAN & HOW CAN I APPLY IT TO MY LIFE TODAY?

_____

_____

_____

_____

_____

_____

_____

PRACTICE & LEARN:

☐ SAY IT OUT LOUD TWICE

☐ DRAW OR DOODLE IT

☐ USE IT IN A PRAYER

☐ SHARE IT WITH OTHERS

NOTES:

BIBLE VERSE: _____ DATE: _____

_____
_____
_____
_____
_____
_____
_____
_____

WHAT DOES IT MEAN & HOW CAN I APPLY IT TO MY LIFE TODAY?

_____

_____

_____

_____

_____

_____

PRACTICE & LEARN:

- ☐ SAY IT OUT LOUD TWICE
- ☐ DRAW OR DOODLE IT
- ☐ USE IT IN A PRAYER
- ☐ SHARE IT WITH OTHERS

NOTES:

BIBLE VERSE: _____ DATE: _____

_____
_____
_____
_____
_____
_____
_____
_____
_____

WHAT DOES IT MEAN & HOW CAN I APPLY IT TO MY LIFE TODAY?

_____
_____
_____
_____
_____
_____

PRACTICE & LEARN:

☑ SAY IT OUT LOUD TWICE

☑ DRAW OR DOODLE IT

☑ USE IT IN A PRAYER

☑ SHARE IT WITH OTHERS

NOTES:

BIBLE VERSE: _____ (DATE: _____)

_____
_____
_____
_____
_____
_____
_____
_____
_____

WHAT DOES IT MEAN & HOW CAN I APPLY IT TO MY LIFE TODAY?

_____
_____
_____
_____
_____
_____
_____

PRACTICE & LEARN:

- ☐ SAY IT OUT LOUD TWICE
- ☐ DRAW OR DOODLE IT
- ☐ USE IT IN A PRAYER
- ☐ SHARE IT WITH OTHERS

NOTES:

BIBLE VERSE: _____ DATE: _____

_____

_____

_____

_____

_____

_____

_____

_____

WHAT DOES IT MEAN & HOW CAN I APPLY IT TO MY LIFE TODAY?

_____

_____

_____

_____

_____

_____

_____

PRACTICE & LEARN:

- ☐ SAY IT OUT LOUD TWICE
- ☐ DRAW OR DOODLE IT
- ☐ USE IT IN A PRAYER
- ☐ SHARE IT WITH OTHERS

NOTES:

BIBLE VERSE: _____ DATE: _____

_____

_____

_____

_____

_____

_____

_____

_____

WHAT DOES IT MEAN & HOW CAN I APPLY IT TO MY LIFE TODAY?

_____

_____

_____

_____

_____

_____

_____

PRACTICE & LEARN:

☐ SAY IT OUT LOUD TWICE

☐ DRAW OR DOODLE IT

☐ USE IT IN A PRAYER

☐ SHARE IT WITH OTHERS

NOTES:

BIBLE VERSE: _____

_____

_____

_____

_____

_____

_____

_____

_____

_____

WHAT DOES IT MEAN & HOW CAN I APPLY IT TO MY LIFE TODAY?

_____

_____

_____

_____

_____

_____

_____

PRACTICE & LEARN:

- ☐ SAY IT OUT LOUD TWICE
- ☐ DRAW OR DOODLE IT
- ☐ USE IT IN A PRAYER
- ☐ SHARE IT WITH OTHERS

NOTES:

BIBLE VERSE: _____ (DATE: _____)

_____
_____
_____
_____
_____
_____
_____
_____
_____

WHAT DOES IT MEAN & HOW CAN I APPLY IT TO MY LIFE TODAY?

_____
_____
_____
_____
_____
_____
_____
_____

PRACTICE & LEARN:

☐ SAY IT OUT LOUD TWICE

☐ DRAW OR DOODLE IT

☐ USE IT IN A PRAYER

☐ SHARE IT WITH OTHERS

NOTES:

BIBLE VERSE: _____ DATE: _____

_____
_____
_____
_____
_____
_____
_____
_____
_____

WHAT DOES IT MEAN & HOW CAN I APPLY IT TO MY LIFE TODAY?

_____
_____
_____
_____
_____
_____

PRACTICE & LEARN:

☐ SAY IT OUT LOUD TWICE

☐ DRAW OR DOODLE IT

☐ USE IT IN A PRAYER

☐ SHARE IT WITH OTHERS

NOTES:

BIBLE VERSE: _____ DATE: _____

_____
_____
_____
_____
_____
_____
_____
_____

WHAT DOES IT MEAN & HOW CAN I APPLY IT TO MY LIFE TODAY?

_____
_____
_____
_____
_____
_____
_____

PRACTICE & LEARN:

☐ SAY IT OUT LOUD TWICE

☐ DRAW OR DOODLE IT

☐ USE IT IN A PRAYER

☐ SHARE IT WITH OTHERS

NOTES:

BIBLE VERSE: _____ DATE: _____

_____
_____
_____
_____
_____
_____
_____
_____
_____

WHAT DOES IT MEAN & HOW CAN I APPLY IT TO MY LIFE TODAY?

_____
_____
_____
_____
_____
_____
_____

PRACTICE & LEARN:

- ☐ SAY IT OUT LOUD TWICE
- ☐ DRAW OR DOODLE IT
- ☐ USE IT IN A PRAYER
- ☐ SHARE IT WITH OTHERS

NOTES:

BIBLE VERSE: _____   DATE: _____

_____
_____
_____
_____
_____
_____
_____
_____
_____

WHAT DOES IT MEAN & HOW CAN I APPLY IT TO MY LIFE TODAY?

_____
_____
_____
_____
_____
_____
_____

PRACTICE & LEARN:

☐ SAY IT OUT LOUD TWICE

☐ DRAW OR DOODLE IT

☐ USE IT IN A PRAYER

☐ SHARE IT WITH OTHERS

NOTES:

BIBLE VERSE: _____ DATE: _____

_____
_____
_____
_____
_____
_____
_____
_____
_____

WHAT DOES IT MEAN & HOW CAN I APPLY IT TO MY LIFE TODAY?

_____

_____

_____

_____

_____

_____

_____

PRACTICE & LEARN:

- ☐ SAY IT OUT LOUD TWICE
- ☐ DRAW OR DOODLE IT
- ☐ USE IT IN A PRAYER
- ☐ SHARE IT WITH OTHERS

NOTES:

BIBLE VERSE: _____ DATE: _____

_____

_____

_____

_____

_____

_____

_____

_____

WHAT DOES IT MEAN & HOW CAN I APPLY IT TO MY LIFE TODAY?

PRACTICE & LEARN:

_____

_____   ☐ SAY IT OUT LOUD TWICE

_____   ☐ DRAW OR DOODLE IT

_____   ☐ USE IT IN A PRAYER

_____   ☐ SHARE IT WITH OTHERS

_____

_____

NOTES:

BIBLE VERSE: _____ DATE: _____

_____

_____

_____

_____

_____

_____

_____

_____

WHAT DOES IT MEAN & HOW CAN I APPLY IT TO MY LIFE TODAY?

_____

_____

_____

_____

_____

_____

_____

PRACTICE & LEARN:

☐ SAY IT OUT LOUD TWICE

☐ DRAW OR DOODLE IT

☐ USE IT IN A PRAYER

☐ SHARE IT WITH OTHERS

NOTES:

BIBLE VERSE: _____ DATE: _____

_____

_____

_____

_____

_____

_____

_____

_____

WHAT DOES IT MEAN & HOW CAN I APPLY IT TO MY LIFE TODAY?

_____

_____

_____

_____

_____

_____

PRACTICE & LEARN:

- ☐ SAY IT OUT LOUD TWICE
- ☐ DRAW OR DOODLE IT
- ☐ USE IT IN A PRAYER
- ☐ SHARE IT WITH OTHERS

NOTES:

BIBLE VERSE: _____ (DATE: _____)

_____
_____
_____
_____
_____
_____
_____
_____

WHAT DOES IT MEAN & HOW CAN I APPLY IT TO MY LIFE TODAY?

_____
_____
_____
_____
_____
_____
_____
_____

PRACTICE & LEARN:

- ☐ SAY IT OUT LOUD TWICE
- ☐ DRAW OR DOODLE IT
- ☐ USE IT IN A PRAYER
- ☐ SHARE IT WITH OTHERS

NOTES:

BIBLE VERSE: _____ DATE: _____

_____

_____

_____

_____

_____

_____

_____

_____

WHAT DOES IT MEAN & HOW CAN I APPLY IT TO MY LIFE TODAY?

_____

_____

_____

_____

_____

_____

_____

PRACTICE & LEARN:

☐ SAY IT OUT LOUD TWICE

☐ DRAW OR DOODLE IT

☐ USE IT IN A PRAYER

☐ SHARE IT WITH OTHERS

NOTES:

BIBLE VERSE: _____ DATE: _____

_____
_____
_____
_____
_____
_____
_____
_____
_____

WHAT DOES IT MEAN & HOW CAN I APPLY IT TO MY LIFE TODAY?

_____
_____
_____
_____
_____
_____
_____
_____

PRACTICE & LEARN:

☐ SAY IT OUT LOUD TWICE

☐ DRAW OR DOODLE IT

☐ USE IT IN A PRAYER

☐ SHARE IT WITH OTHERS

NOTES:

BIBLE VERSE: _____   DATE: _____

_____

_____

_____

_____

_____

_____

_____

_____

_____

WHAT DOES IT MEAN & HOW CAN I APPLY IT TO MY LIFE TODAY?

_____

_____

_____

_____

_____

_____

_____

PRACTICE & LEARN:

☐ SAY IT OUT LOUD TWICE

☐ DRAW OR DOODLE IT

☐ USE IT IN A PRAYER

☐ SHARE IT WITH OTHERS

NOTES:

BIBLE VERSE: _____ (DATE: _____)

_____
_____
_____
_____
_____
_____
_____
_____

WHAT DOES IT MEAN & HOW CAN I APPLY IT TO MY LIFE TODAY?

_____

_____

_____

_____

_____

_____

PRACTICE & LEARN:

- ☐ SAY IT OUT LOUD TWICE
- ☐ DRAW OR DOODLE IT
- ☐ USE IT IN A PRAYER
- ☐ SHARE IT WITH OTHERS

NOTES:

BIBLE VERSE: _____ DATE: _____

_____
_____
_____
_____
_____
_____
_____
_____

WHAT DOES IT MEAN & HOW CAN I APPLY IT TO MY LIFE TODAY?

_____

_____

_____

_____

_____

_____

PRACTICE & LEARN:

- ☐ SAY IT OUT LOUD TWICE
- ☐ DRAW OR DOODLE IT
- ☐ USE IT IN A PRAYER
- ☐ SHARE IT WITH OTHERS

NOTES:

BIBLE VERSE: _____ DATE: _____

_____
_____
_____
_____
_____
_____
_____
_____
_____

WHAT DOES iT MEAN & HOW CAN i APPLY iT TO MY LiFE TODAY?

_____
_____
_____
_____
_____
_____
_____
_____

PRACTICE & LEARN:

- ☐ SAY iT OUT LOUD TWiCE
- ☐ DRAW OR DOODLE iT
- ☐ USE iT iN A PRAYER
- ☐ SHARE iT WiTH OTHERS

NOTES:

BIBLE VERSE: _____ DATE: _____

_____

_____

_____

_____

_____

_____

_____

_____

WHAT DOES IT MEAN & HOW CAN I APPLY IT TO MY LIFE TODAY?

_____

_____

_____

_____

_____

_____

_____

PRACTICE & LEARN:

- ☐ SAY IT OUT LOUD TWICE
- ☐ DRAW OR DOODLE IT
- ☐ USE IT IN A PRAYER
- ☐ SHARE IT WITH OTHERS

NOTES:

BIBLE VERSE: _____ (DATE: _____)

_____
_____
_____
_____
_____
_____
_____
_____

WHAT DOES IT MEAN & HOW CAN I APPLY IT TO MY LIFE TODAY?

_____
_____
_____
_____
_____
_____
_____

PRACTICE & LEARN:

☐ SAY IT OUT LOUD TWICE

☐ DRAW OR DOODLE IT

☐ USE IT IN A PRAYER

☐ SHARE IT WITH OTHERS

NOTES:

BIBLE VERSE: _____ DATE: _____

_____

_____

_____

_____

_____

_____

_____

_____

WHAT DOES IT MEAN & HOW CAN I APPLY IT TO MY LIFE TODAY?

_____

_____

_____

_____

_____

_____

_____

PRACTICE & LEARN:

☐ SAY IT OUT LOUD TWICE

☐ DRAW OR DOODLE IT

☐ USE IT IN A PRAYER

☐ SHARE IT WITH OTHERS

NOTES:

BIBLE VERSE: _____ DATE: _____

_____
_____
_____
_____
_____
_____
_____
_____
_____

WHAT DOES IT MEAN & HOW CAN I APPLY IT TO MY LIFE TODAY?

_____
_____
_____
_____
_____
_____

PRACTICE & LEARN:

- ☐ SAY IT OUT LOUD TWICE
- ☐ DRAW OR DOODLE IT
- ☐ USE IT IN A PRAYER
- ☐ SHARE IT WITH OTHERS

NOTES:

BIBLE VERSE: _____ DATE: _____

_____
_____
_____
_____
_____
_____
_____
_____
_____

WHAT DOES IT MEAN & HOW CAN I APPLY IT TO MY LIFE TODAY?

_____
_____
_____
_____
_____
_____
_____

PRACTICE & LEARN:

☐ SAY IT OUT LOUD TWICE

☐ DRAW OR DOODLE IT

☐ USE IT IN A PRAYER

☐ SHARE IT WITH OTHERS

NOTES:

BIBLE VERSE: _____ DATE: _____

_____

_____

_____

_____

_____

_____

_____

_____

WHAT DOES IT MEAN & HOW CAN I APPLY IT TO MY LIFE TODAY?

_____

_____

_____

_____

_____

_____

PRACTICE & LEARN:

- ☐ SAY IT OUT LOUD TWICE
- ☐ DRAW OR DOODLE IT
- ☐ USE IT IN A PRAYER
- ☐ SHARE IT WITH OTHERS

NOTES:

BIBLE VERSE: _____ DATE: _____

_____
_____
_____
_____
_____
_____
_____
_____
_____

WHAT DOES IT MEAN & HOW CAN I APPLY IT TO MY LIFE TODAY?

PRACTICE & LEARN:

_____
_____   ☐ SAY IT OUT LOUD TWICE
_____
_____   ☐ DRAW OR DOODLE IT
_____
_____   ☐ USE IT IN A PRAYER
_____
                                     ☐ SHARE IT WITH OTHERS

NOTES:

BIBLE VERSE: _____ DATE: _____

_____
_____
_____
_____
_____
_____
_____
_____

WHAT DOES IT MEAN & HOW CAN I APPLY IT TO MY LIFE TODAY?

_____
_____
_____
_____
_____
_____
_____

PRACTICE & LEARN:

- ☐ SAY IT OUT LOUD TWICE
- ☐ DRAW OR DOODLE IT
- ☐ USE IT IN A PRAYER
- ☐ SHARE IT WITH OTHERS

NOTES:

BIBLE VERSE: _____ DATE: _____

_____
_____
_____
_____
_____
_____
_____
_____
_____

WHAT DOES IT MEAN & HOW CAN I APPLY IT TO MY LIFE TODAY?

_____
_____
_____
_____
_____
_____
_____

PRACTICE & LEARN:

☐ SAY IT OUT LOUD TWICE

☐ DRAW OR DOODLE IT

☐ USE IT IN A PRAYER

☐ SHARE IT WITH OTHERS

NOTES:

BIBLE VERSE: _____ DATE: _____

_____

_____

_____

_____

_____

_____

_____

WHAT DOES IT MEAN & HOW CAN I APPLY IT TO MY LIFE TODAY?

_____

_____

_____

_____

_____

_____

PRACTICE & LEARN:

- ☐ SAY IT OUT LOUD TWICE
- ☐ DRAW OR DOODLE IT
- ☐ USE IT IN A PRAYER
- ☐ SHARE IT WITH OTHERS

NOTES:

BIBLE VERSE: _____ DATE: _____

_____
_____
_____
_____
_____
_____
_____
_____
_____

WHAT DOES IT MEAN & HOW CAN I APPLY IT TO MY LIFE TODAY?

_____

_____

_____

_____

_____

_____

PRACTICE & LEARN:

- ☐ SAY IT OUT LOUD TWICE
- ☐ DRAW OR DOODLE IT
- ☐ USE IT IN A PRAYER
- ☐ SHARE IT WITH OTHERS

NOTES:

BIBLE VERSE: _____ DATE: _____

_____

_____

_____

_____

_____

_____

_____

_____

WHAT DOES IT MEAN & HOW CAN I APPLY IT TO MY LIFE TODAY?

_____

_____

_____

_____

_____

_____

_____

PRACTICE & LEARN:

☐ SAY IT OUT LOUD TWICE

☐ DRAW OR DOODLE IT

☐ USE IT IN A PRAYER

☐ SHARE IT WITH OTHERS

NOTES:

BIBLE VERSE: _____ DATE: _____

_____

_____

_____

_____

_____

_____

_____

_____

WHAT DOES IT MEAN & HOW CAN I APPLY IT TO MY LIFE TODAY?

_____

_____

_____

_____

_____

_____

PRACTICE & LEARN:

- ☐ SAY IT OUT LOUD TWICE
- ☐ DRAW OR DOODLE IT
- ☐ USE IT IN A PRAYER
- ☐ SHARE IT WITH OTHERS

NOTES:

BIBLE VERSE: _____ DATE: _____

_____
_____
_____
_____
_____
_____
_____
_____

WHAT DOES IT MEAN & HOW CAN I APPLY IT TO MY LIFE TODAY?

_____

_____

_____

_____

_____

_____

PRACTICE & LEARN:

- ☐ SAY IT OUT LOUD TWICE
- ☐ DRAW OR DOODLE IT
- ☐ USE IT IN A PRAYER
- ☐ SHARE IT WITH OTHERS

NOTES:

BIBLE VERSE: _____ DATE: _____

_____
_____
_____
_____
_____
_____
_____
_____

WHAT DOES IT MEAN & HOW CAN I APPLY IT TO MY LIFE TODAY?

_____

_____

_____

_____

_____

_____

_____

PRACTICE & LEARN:

☐ SAY IT OUT LOUD TWICE

☐ DRAW OR DOODLE IT

☐ USE IT IN A PRAYER

☐ SHARE IT WITH OTHERS

NOTES:

BIBLE VERSE:_____ DATE:_____

_____
_____
_____
_____
_____
_____
_____
_____

WHAT DOES IT MEAN & HOW CAN I APPLY IT TO MY LIFE TODAY?

_____
_____
_____
_____
_____
_____
_____

PRACTICE & LEARN:

- ☐ SAY IT OUT LOUD TWICE
- ☐ DRAW OR DOODLE IT
- ☐ USE IT IN A PRAYER
- ☐ SHARE IT WITH OTHERS

NOTES:

BIBLE VERSE: _____ DATE: _____

_____
_____
_____
_____
_____
_____
_____
_____

WHAT DOES IT MEAN & HOW CAN I APPLY IT TO MY LIFE TODAY?

_____
_____
_____
_____
_____
_____

PRACTICE & LEARN:

- ☐ SAY IT OUT LOUD TWICE
- ☐ DRAW OR DOODLE IT
- ☐ USE IT IN A PRAYER
- ☐ SHARE IT WITH OTHERS

NOTES:

BIBLE VERSE: _____ (DATE: _____)

_____
_____
_____
_____
_____
_____
_____
_____
_____

WHAT DOES IT MEAN & HOW CAN I APPLY IT TO MY LIFE TODAY?

_____

_____

_____

_____

_____

_____

_____

PRACTICE & LEARN:

- ☐ SAY IT OUT LOUD TWICE
- ☐ DRAW OR DOODLE IT
- ☐ USE IT IN A PRAYER
- ☐ SHARE IT WITH OTHERS

NOTES:

BIBLE VERSE: _____ (DATE: _____)

_____

_____

_____

_____

_____

_____

_____

_____

_____

WHAT DOES IT MEAN & HOW CAN I APPLY IT TO MY LIFE TODAY?

_____

_____

_____

_____

_____

_____

_____

PRACTICE & LEARN:

- ☐ SAY IT OUT LOUD TWICE
- ☐ DRAW OR DOODLE IT
- ☐ USE IT IN A PRAYER
- ☐ SHARE IT WITH OTHERS

NOTES:

BIBLE VERSE: _____ DATE: _____

_____
_____
_____
_____
_____
_____
_____
_____

WHAT DOES IT MEAN & HOW CAN I APPLY IT TO MY LIFE TODAY?

_____
_____
_____
_____
_____
_____
_____

PRACTICE & LEARN:

- ☐ SAY IT OUT LOUD TWICE
- ☐ DRAW OR DOODLE IT
- ☐ USE IT IN A PRAYER
- ☐ SHARE IT WITH OTHERS

NOTES:

BIBLE VERSE: _____ DATE: _____

_____
_____
_____
_____
_____
_____
_____
_____

WHAT DOES IT MEAN & HOW CAN I APPLY IT TO MY LIFE TODAY?

_____

_____

_____

_____

_____

_____

_____

PRACTICE & LEARN:

- ☐ SAY IT OUT LOUD TWICE
- ☐ DRAW OR DOODLE IT
- ☐ USE IT IN A PRAYER
- ☐ SHARE IT WITH OTHERS

NOTES:

BIBLE VERSE: _____ DATE: _____

_____
_____
_____
_____
_____
_____
_____
_____

WHAT DOES IT MEAN & HOW CAN I APPLY IT TO MY LIFE TODAY?

_____
_____
_____
_____
_____
_____

PRACTICE & LEARN:

- ☐ SAY IT OUT LOUD TWICE
- ☐ DRAW OR DOODLE IT
- ☐ USE IT IN A PRAYER
- ☐ SHARE IT WITH OTHERS

NOTES:

BIBLE VERSE: _____ DATE: _____

_____

_____

_____

_____

_____

_____

_____

_____

WHAT DOES IT MEAN & HOW CAN I APPLY IT TO MY LIFE TODAY?

_____

_____

_____

_____

_____

_____

_____

PRACTICE & LEARN:

☐ SAY IT OUT LOUD TWICE

☐ DRAW OR DOODLE IT

☐ USE IT IN A PRAYER

☐ SHARE IT WITH OTHERS

NOTES:

BIBLE VERSE: _____ DATE: _____

_____

_____

_____

_____

_____

_____

_____

_____

WHAT DOES IT MEAN & HOW CAN I APPLY IT TO MY LIFE TODAY?

_____

_____

_____

_____

_____

_____

_____

PRACTICE & LEARN:

- ☐ SAY IT OUT LOUD TWICE
- ☐ DRAW OR DOODLE IT
- ☐ USE IT IN A PRAYER
- ☐ SHARE IT WITH OTHERS

NOTES:

BIBLE VERSE: _____ DATE: _____

_____
_____
_____
_____
_____
_____
_____
_____

WHAT DOES IT MEAN & HOW CAN I APPLY IT TO MY LIFE TODAY?

_____

_____

_____

_____

_____

_____

_____

PRACTICE & LEARN:

☐ SAY IT OUT LOUD TWICE

☐ DRAW OR DOODLE IT

☐ USE IT IN A PRAYER

☐ SHARE IT WITH OTHERS

NOTES:

BIBLE VERSE: _____

_____
_____
_____
_____
_____
_____
_____
_____

WHAT DOES IT MEAN & HOW CAN I APPLY IT TO MY LIFE TODAY?

_____
_____
_____
_____
_____
_____
_____

PRACTICE & LEARN:

- ☐ SAY IT OUT LOUD TWICE
- ☐ DRAW OR DOODLE IT
- ☐ USE IT IN A PRAYER
- ☐ SHARE IT WITH OTHERS

NOTES:

BIBLE VERSE: _____ DATE: _____

_____

_____

_____

_____

_____

_____

_____

_____

WHAT DOES IT MEAN & HOW CAN I APPLY IT TO MY LIFE TODAY?

_____

_____

_____

_____

_____

_____

_____

PRACTICE & LEARN:

☐ SAY IT OUT LOUD TWICE

☐ DRAW OR DOODLE IT

☐ USE IT IN A PRAYER

☐ SHARE IT WITH OTHERS

NOTES:

BIBLE VERSE: _____ DATE: _____

_____
_____
_____
_____
_____
_____
_____
_____

WHAT DOES IT MEAN & HOW CAN I APPLY IT TO MY LIFE TODAY?

_____
_____
_____
_____
_____
_____

PRACTICE & LEARN:

- ☐ SAY IT OUT LOUD TWICE
- ☐ DRAW OR DOODLE IT
- ☐ USE IT IN A PRAYER
- ☐ SHARE IT WITH OTHERS

NOTES:

BIBLE VERSE: _____ DATE: _____

_____
_____
_____
_____
_____
_____
_____
_____

WHAT DOES IT MEAN & HOW CAN I APPLY IT TO MY LIFE TODAY?

_____

_____

_____

_____

_____

_____

PRACTICE & LEARN:

☐ SAY IT OUT LOUD TWICE

☐ DRAW OR DOODLE IT

☐ USE IT IN A PRAYER

☐ SHARE IT WITH OTHERS

NOTES:

MY ADDITIONAL NOTES:

MY ADDITIONAL NOTES:

Made in United States
Troutdale, OR
08/24/2023

12320439R00064